# The Night Runner

by

## Alan Combes

Illustrated by Dylan Gibson

# To Gervase Phinn,
## the best inspector who called

With special thanks to:

Felix Allan

Holly Anderson

Callum Davidson

Aaron Dickson

Sam Egerton

Maggie Girrity

Janine Hickman

Pam Reid

Stewart Shaw

Ben Thomson

First published in 2009 in Great Britain by
Barrington Stoke Ltd
18 Walker St, Edinburgh, EH3 7LP

www.barringtonstoke.co.uk

ISBN: 978-1-84299-659-1

Printed in Great Britain by Bell & Bain Ltd

# Contents

# Chapter 1
# Greg's Bad Day

Greg Green was running the school mile on Sports Day at school.  He told his mum and dad that he could win it.  He told his friends in the same class at school that he could win it.

"I'm fast," he told them.  "At Junior School I won every year."

But on the day of the race, he was nervous.  As he was putting on his trainers in the dressing room, he looked at some of the other runners.  They were wearing proper running shoes; shoes with spikes that would help them get a better grip.

There were 10 runners in the race.  Greg walked to the start and saw that nearly all of them were taller than him.  He saw their leg muscles too.  They all looked stronger than him.  Maybe this race was not going to be that easy after all.

They lined up at the start and Greg's mates were yelling for him.

"Go for it, Greg! You gotta be fast from the start."

The gun fired and Greg went to the front. He felt good and stayed in front all the way round the first lap. But after that he began puffing a lot so he dropped back. Three, four, then five runners overtook him. No worry. He would just run behind them until the last lap. Then he would sprint past them all.

The problem was that he was now feeling awful. He felt sick and could taste his dinner at the back of his mouth.

There was just one lap to go. Maybe Greg was next to last, but here was his chance to get up to the front.

Suddenly all the runners were speeding up and even the boy behind him went past.

When Greg crossed the finish line, he was nearly 50 metres behind the 9th runner.

To make it even worse, he sicked up his dinner as he crossed the line.

His friends did not cheer him like a winner. They were falling about laughing. Danny Wood, his enemy, came over to him and patted him on the back.

"I think I saw a tortoise overtake you at the end there, Greg," Danny said.

Even his mate Jed said, "You aren't very fit, are you, Greg?"

Greg's dad was waiting for him when he got home. "Where did you finish, Greg?" he asked at once.

"I didn't win, Dad. I came 10th," Greg answered. It was better than saying he'd come last.

"Never mind, there's always next year," his dad said.

Luckily, his mum and dad didn't ask him how many runners were in the race. That would have made him really ashamed.

But Greg made his mind up. He was never going to be made a fool of again like that. Next year he would be ready for the race. Next year he would make Danny Wood smile on the other side of his face. Next year his friends would be cheering his victory.

That weekend Greg made his plans.

# Chapter 2
# The Plan

First he must lose some fat. His dad had joked only last week, "You're getting quite a belly on you, Greg. Time to give up the beer."

Then he would get some proper running gear. He would ask his parents to give it to him for his birthday. He would get shorts, vest and a warm tracksuit.  Then he would save up the money from his paper round to buy some proper running shoes; shoes with spikes.

Last and most important of all, he would get fit.  Instead of riding the bike on his paper round, he would jog.  That would get rid of the fat too.

Getting fit is one thing. But he also needed to run faster. When he had run in the school mile, he had been left far behind on that last lap. He talked to his dad about how to run fast.

"You need a fast finish," his dad said. "I've seen it on T.V. The runner who speeds up at the end often wins."

That was what made up his mind. He would not tell anyone. Not his mum, his dad, nor his friends. Each night he would go in the dark to the school field and practise running a lap as fast as he could.

He would make up a story that he was going to the Youth Club. That way his parents would not ask him where he had been. They knew he often went to the Youth Club in his tracksuit.

He would keep it a secret because he did not want people like Danny Wood to know what he was doing. They would only tease him.

Nor would he tell his mate Jed. The best way to keep a secret is to tell no one.

Greg made himself wait till the weather was warmer. Soon winter was over and it was time to start getting ready for the big race.

# Chapter 3
# A Dark Shape

The moon-light was so bright that Greg could see the school field as clearly as if it was day time. He had already run four laps. He felt tired. Now was the time to run a very fast lap, like he would have to in the school mile.

His arms pumped up and down, his legs pushed with all their power. He was on the far side of the field where there was a wood. The trees made it darker.

Suddenly Greg felt scared, but he couldn't see why. His heart was banging away ... and it wasn't just because of the running. He slowed down and looked over at the trees.

There was something among the trees.  A dark shape.  Was it a man?  No, it was too big to be a man.  So was it an animal?  What if it was half man and half animal?  If it attacked and hurt him, Greg was alone.  There was no one to help him.

By now he was very scared.  What if the shape ran out of the trees and attacked him?  He sprinted as fast as he had ever done in his life.  His speed carried him all the way to the bottom end of the track.  The finish was next to the school gate.

Out of breath, he fell to his knees.  When he had got his breath back, he looked across the field.  He could see nothing to be scared of. Maybe it had been a tree with a weird

shape. Perhaps his mind was playing tricks.

But the fear had been real. He knew that. It felt as though someone – or something – had been chasing him.

Worn out, he scrambled over the gate and jogged home. He was tired, but he felt good about his running.

"Where have you been, Greg?" his dad said when he got home.

"I've been to the Youth Club," Greg lied.

"But you're wearing your tracksuit and you're all damp with sweat," his dad said.

"Been playing five-a-side footy, Dad," Greg told him.

He didn't like telling lies to his dad, but that was part of keeping his plan a secret. So he could not tell him about the dark shape he had seen in the trees.

# Chapter 4
# A Change of Plan

Greg had been scared that night, but he so wanted to win that race. He made his mind up to train at the school field four nights a week. He would do it, shape or no shape; ghost or no ghost.

The next time he went to the track, it was a very black night. He ran with a head torch which lit up the track in front of him. There were no dark scary shapes under the trees, so he did his four laps and went home.

On the Friday night, the moon was out again. Three laps into his training, he saw the shape again. It was in the same place. Once again, Greg was very scared and ran his fastest away from it.

"Dad!" he yelled, but Dad was not there. No one could help him.

At one point he looked back and he was sure he could see the shape on the track. It was about 100 metres behind him. It was man-shaped, but much taller. He tried to make out the shape of its head. It looked like it was wearing a helmet. He leapt over the gate and raced home.

That night when he went home, it was hard to say nothing to his dad. If only his dad had been at the school field, then maybe they could have worked out what the shape was. Could it have been someone fooling around in fancy dress? Greg did not think so.

Something had to be done or his plan would fall apart. He would be too scared to train.

The next day at school Greg changed his mind and spoke to Jed, his best friend.

"Jed, if I tell you a secret, will you promise to keep it?"

"Of course, Greg. We've been mates since we were kids," Jed said.

"Jed, do you believe in ghosts?" Greg asked.

"Well, I've never met one," Jed said.

Greg then told Jed about his plans to win the race. He told him about his secret runs at night on the school track. He told him about the weird shape in the trees.

"Wow!" was all Jed could say. "So what do you think it is?"

"I don't know," Greg told him, "but it would help me if you could come to the track each night. It would help to have someone else there."

"Great!" Jed said. "We could go ghost hunting."

Greg wasn't sure about that.

Then Jed added, "I'm up for it. When do we go?"

# Chapter 5
# Running Scared

On Sunday night Jed met Greg at the school gate at seven o'clock.

"It's dark out here, isn't it?" Jed said.

"No moon tonight.  I don't think we'll see it," Greg said.

Greg had worked out the link.
Moon-light made the shape thing come. No
moon and there was no shape.

And it was true. No shape came that
night.

Jed watched Greg do his training. Then
they went home.

"What a waste of time that was," Jed said to him at school next day.

"Sorry," Greg said. "I can't press a button and make it appear."

The big race was just two weeks away so Greg trained five nights that week. The first night that the moon was out, he phoned Jed.

"The moon's out. Meet me at the track tonight."

Jed turned up in his tracksuit so he could run a lap or two with Greg.

"Where does the shape appear?" he asked.

"Over there," said Greg, pointing to a line of tall trees.

Nothing happened until Greg had done his fast lap.

"Wow, that was hard," he told Jed, puffing loudly.

At first Jed said nothing. He stood there like he was made of stone. His eyes were fixed on the woods.

Then Jed spoke. "It's moving. Can you see it?"

There were tears in his voice. "I think it means to get us."

The two of them rushed across the school
field to the fence. Greg waited for Jed and
saw the shape getting closer.

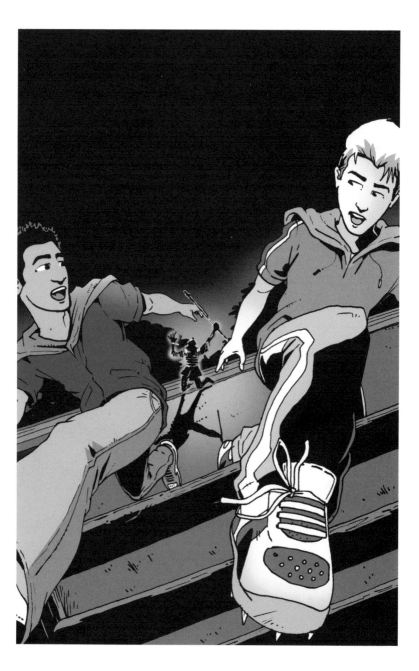

Suddenly it stopped.  It was hard to see in the dark but it had fallen down to its knees.  Greg and Jed jumped the fence on to the main road.

"What happened?" Greg asked, looking back.

"Let's get out of here," Jed said, and the two of them ran towards the town.

Once they were clear, Greg said, "It's the race next week.  I won't be coming back here to train."

# Chapter 6
# The Big Race

Jed kept Greg's secret. He never told anyone about Greg's training or about the shape thing.

"Think you'll win today?" he asked Greg on the morning of the race.

"I couldn't be fitter," Greg told him, "and my plan is to finish really fast."

There was a shock for him when Greg got to the changing rooms. Danny Wood was there. His enemy, Danny Wood, was in the race. Danny Wood, who had called him a tortoise after last year's race.

"Think you've got a chance?" Danny asked.

"As good a chance as you," Greg said.

The race was slow this year. No one wanted to take the lead. All the runners were bunched up together. Greg was in the middle.

That was when he felt someone's foot trip him up. Greg lost his balance and fell over. He heard Danny's laugh and he knew that he had done it just to put Greg out of the race.

By the time he got up, the runners were far in front.

Now Greg had to remember all the planning and training. It made him feel so angry that he chased after the others.

With one lap to go he was level with the last man.

He had to remember the shape and how he had used his fear of it to sprint. That's what he did now. His spikes dug into the track and with 100 metres left, there was only Danny Wood between him and winning.

"See you, Danny," Greg said as he sailed past him.

This year no one was laughing at Greg. Jed and his mates cheered madly as Greg broke the tape.

When the cheering was over, Jed found Greg.

"You need to come over to the Javelin," Jed told him. "You need to see this."

Greg saw how white Jed's face was.

# Chapter 7
# Solving the Mystery

On the other side of the field, Rob Smith had thrown the javelin a record distance. By the time Greg and Jed had arrived, Mrs Cropper, the head teacher, was there too.

She was there because the javelin had landed in the grass and hit a bone. A human bone. Funny ... it was next to

where the scary shape had fallen to its
knees.

"Stand back, everyone," said Mrs
Cropper, the head, "the police are on their
way."

"There used to be a Roman village where
our school is now," she said, "and I think
Rob's javelin has hit a skeleton!"

When the police came, everyone had to go back indoors. Greg had a shower and changed before going back to his class.

"You'll never guess what Mr Turner just told us," Jed said.

Mr Turner was a history teacher so he knew about stuff like the Romans and digging up remains.

"He said that the skeleton had been a really tall man," Jed said.

Now Mr Turner spoke to the class. "They found a helmet next to the bones."

"Who was the skeleton, sir?" Greg asked.

"I think he was the sentry for the Roman village that was here," Mr Turner said.

"What's a sentry, sir?" they asked Mr Turner.

"A kind of look-out," he said. "He kept watch while everyone slept."

"I don't get it," Greg said to Jed when they were walking home.

"What's to get?" Jed said. "When you were running on the school track at nights – doing your training – you must have seen a ghost."

"The look-out, you mean?" Greg asked.

"I looked it up on the internet," Jed said. "In those days, if the sentry fell asleep when he was on look-out, he was in big trouble."

"What kind of trouble?" Greg asked.

"The rest of the soldiers often killed him as a punishment."

So Greg understood now. The ghost of the sentry must have stayed on look-out where he was buried ever since.

"Thanks to that sentry I won the school mile," Greg told Jed.

"You're right," Jed said. "Being chased by a ghost did you one big favour."

But Greg would train in daylight from now on. He never wanted to be that scared again.

# Killer Croc

## by
## S. P. Gates

Levi is in danger. There's a Killer Croc on the loose – and it's hungry. Can he escape its jaws?

You can order *Killer Croc* from our website at
www.barringtonstoke.co.uk

# *Flash Flood*

## by
## Andy Croft

Jaz and Toni are trapped and the water is rising ...
Can they make it out in time?

# *Cliff Edge*

## by
## Jane A. C. West

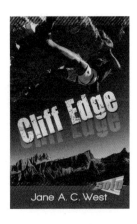

Can Danny make the climb of his life to save his friend? No ropes, no help – no hope?

You can order *Cliff Edge* from our website at www.barringtonstoke.co.uk

# *Snow Dogs*

## by
## Jane A. C. West

Zeb wants to win the dog sled race.
But will he die before he gets
to the finish?

# *United Here I Come!*

## by
## Alan Combes

Joey and Jimmy are very bad at football.
But Jimmy is sure he will play for
United one day.
Is Jimmy crazy – or will he get there?

You can order *United Here I Come!* from our website at
www.barringtonstoke.co.uk